# FIDO'S FOUL SURPRISE

# FIDO'S FOUL SURPRISE

## And Other 'Ruff' Rhymes

### *by*
### Gez Walsh

### Illustrated by the author

# The King's England Press
## 2001

ISBN 1 872438 75 X

*Fido's Foul Surprise* is typeset by Moose Manuscripts
in Times New Roman 13pt and published by
The King's England Press,
Cambertown House, Commercial Road, Goldthorpe,
Rotherham, South Yorkshire, S63 9BL

Printed and bound in Great Britain by:

Woolnough Bookbinding
Irthlingborough
Northamptonshire

# Author's note

This is a new collection of dubious ditties with a twist (from a twisted mind).

These poems, or whatever you wish to call them, should be enjoyed by adults and children together. Yes, even the underdeveloped and innocent minds of adults will be able to laugh, along with the street-wise, intelligent children, though most adults may need some of the poems explained.

As with all my books, I wish to encourage children to read. Hopefully, both children *and* adults will enjoy this latest book and maybe by sharing the experience, more children will be encouraged into the habit of reading.

If, for whatever reason, you don't enjoy this book, please let my publisher know so they can send the boys round to change your mind!

*Gez Walsh*

# Fank Yers

Steve (doggie doo doos) Rudd
Debbie (the pong that rises) Nunn
Phil (it's got to have a good title) Rendell.
To all the teachers and pupils whose schools I have visited: thanks for making me welcome and for the teachers' dodgy dancing!

**Dedicated to Carol**

## Fido's Foul Surprise

I can't go home tonight,
My dog has caused me grief.
If I were to meet my big brother
I would surely lose my teeth.

I can see why he's angry,
Yes, I too would be upset,
But I wasn't the one
That poohed in his crash helmet!

Mum said he's so angry
That his face is burning red
Because he didn't see it
Until he'd put it on his head!

# Boy Called Pete

There was a young boy called Pete,
Who found an old toffee in the street.
He said, "Isn't it disgusting,
It only needs dusting
And I could give it my sister to eat!"

# Squirty

I have a strange teacher
Who spits when he talks,
And there's a strange squeak
From his shoes when he walks.

I wish he wouldn't spit,
It's such a dirty habit,
Maybe it's his mouth
Filled with the teeth of a rabbit.

We call him Squirty
And keep well back,
Unless when he talks
You're wearing a mac!

## Lost Love

I met a gorgeous boy
At a dance at school,
But I can't face him now,
I feel such a fool.

We got on so well,
Everything was going fine,
We talked, we snogged,
Having a very good time.

The night was so good,
But I went and spoiled it,
By rushing back to him
After visiting the toilet.

I walked across the floor
In the middle of a dance,
My boyfriend then told me
I had my skirt tucked in my pants!

My friend says I should see him,
She's sure we could sort it out,
But to make matters worse
I'd had my knickers on inside out!

## The Purrfect Meal

I put some cat food in the fridge,
It was in an airtight carton.
When I went to feed the cat
I noticed it had gone

Well, the cat was still hungry
So I gave him a fish slice,
Then my sister entered the kitchen
Saying, "Mmh... that tuna was nice!"

I hadn't the heart to tell her
That she thought cat food was nice,
I'll just have to keep an eye on her
In case she starts to chase mice!


## Slap Head Pop

My dad is going bald,
His head's growing through his hair.
Although he tries to hide it,
My mum she doesn't care.

She say's that she loves him,
That it was meant to be,
And I should stop mocking him
Because it might happen to me!

# Am I in Love?

I think I love my girlfriend
But I'm not so sure.
Do you have to love for life
Or is there some kind of cure?

I don't want to get married
And have children of my own,
I'm not ready to settle down -
At thirteen, I can't afford a home.

I want to tour the world,
I want to have some fun!
Go swimming with dolphins,
Sleep under a foreign sun.

You know, while I've been thinking
About all of the above,
Something strange has happened -
I've just fallen out of love!


# Rules

Parents, they have two rules,
That is plain to see.
There's one rule for them,
And a different one for me!

# Granny and the Queen

Granny won an award,
She said, "It's like a dream!"
Because it was to be given
By Her Majesty the Queen.

So Granny bought a new dress,
And knickers for underneath,
Then took a trip to the dentist
For a new set of gleaming teeth.

Then came the big day,
Granny looked so smart,
But she was so full of nerves
When she spoke she let out a fart!

Grandad said not to worry,
It would stop in due course,
And you can't be meeting the Queen
While farting like an old cart-horse.

Her big moment arrived,
She stood before the Queen,
But gave a cough and then let off
The biggest fart you've ever seen!

The Queen's husband was horrified,
Granny didn't know what to do,
But the Queen just smiled then asked
Politely, "Could one perhaps join you?"

Granny just shrugged her shoulders,
Her nerves now torn apart,
Then the Queen shut one eye, lifted her leg
And let off a humungous fart!

Granny said, "Well, I never!
Of all the things I've seen,
I would never have expected this
From Her Majesty the Queen!"

The Queen held Granny's hand
Saying, "They say our blood is blue,
But royalty is still human
And we have to fart just like you!"

That's why she's on playing cards
And famous in many parts,
The favourite queen of the pack
Is always the Queen of Farts!

## My New Girlfriend

I have a new girlfriend,
She has dyed green hair.
I think she looks cool
But mum doesn't like her.

She says she's too rude,
That her attitude is bad -
I think she's got a nerve
Because she married my dad!

## The Oo Mi Goolie Bird

I shall tell you a story,
Of which you may have heard,
About a very strange creature,
A very strange bird.
It's called an Oo Mi Goolie
And I shall now tell you why,
It's such a wonderful sight
When it's high in the sky.
But it has no legs
And the golden rule is
When it lands among rocks
It screams, "Oo Mi Goolies!"

## Marco Polo

Once an Italian explorer,
Marco Polo was his name,
Travelled to China
Where he found fame.
He returned with many objects
That made hearts beat faster,
From fine silks to jewels,
He even gave Italy pasta.
But when my teacher asked me
What was Marco Polo's historical role?
I said, "Didn't he invent the mint with a hole?"

## The Neat Writer

James is in big trouble
For writing in the snow.
He'd written so neatly
But to the head he had to go.

In the middle of the playground,
There for all to see
He had written his name
While he was having a wee!

# How to Wake Up with a Smile!

I shall give you a tip
On how to wake up with a smile,
Please give me a chance
And listen awhile,
For it's proven to work,
From the north to the south,
To wake up with a smile
Sleep with coat hanger in mouth!

# Big Bill Butler

Builder Big Bill Butler
Is a builder in the town,
He builds things up
And he knocks things down.

If you ask him for a price,
No matter what's to do,
He takes a deep breath
And says, "It'll cost you!"

## Don't Pick Yer Scab with Yer Pen

I had a cut on my arm
Which had formed a scab,
I did it falling off my bike
And hitting a concrete slab.

I often used to pick it,
"Oh, no!" I hear you groan,
But there's something about scabs,
You just can't leave them alone.

Once I tried to pick it
With my fountain pen
But I was pushed in the back
By that stupid Ben.

The pen stabbed into my scab
And ink ran out so blue -
Now I don't have a scab
But I've got a strange tattoo.

## Young Girl Called Liz

There was a young girl called Liz,
Who thought she was a whiz.
But she was a right Herbert,
She ate too much sherbet,
Causing her wee-wee to fizz.

# Wilma the Cow

There was once a cow named Wilma
Who lived out in a field
But the farmer wanted rid of her
Because no milk did she yield.

Wilma couldn't eat grass
Which was a problem for her,
She had red eyes and a snotty nose
Suffering from hay fever.

"Cows don't get hay fever!"
The farmer was heard to say.
"Cows eat nothing but grass
And in winter they eat hay."

The farmer called for the vet
Who confirmed what Wilma had.
He said, "Yes, it's hay fever -
For a cow, that's really bad."

The vet said, "Keep her indoors
And it will soon stop."
"No!" replied the farmer
"She will have to go for the chop."

"But you can't kill old Wilma!"
Screamed the farmer's wife.
The farmer said, "She's of no use,
I'll go and get my knife."

The vet agreed with the farmer.
"You will have to move her."
The farmer's wife had an idea -
She ran and fetched her Hoover

Saying, "Hay fever is caused by pollen
So this should work a treat.
If Wilma hoovers the field as she goes
The grass should be safe to eat

So every day for a month
Wilma was a very happy lass
As she hoovered up the pollen
Then ate up all the grass.

Wilma had never been as happy,
Now her hay fever didn't matter;
She started to produce milk
And even became a little fatter.

Soon the people from the television
Heard of poor Wilma's plight
So they sent along a man with a beard,
Yes, Rolf turned up that night.

He asked poor Wilma questions,
Like why? Who? And how?
The farmer said, "Why ask her?
Can't you see she's a cow?"

Rolf said, "She must be clever!"
But that wasn't true.
If he'd seen the farmer's knife,
He'd have vacced the field too!

But viewers saw the knife,
Some even began to sob.
A national newspaper phoned
To offer poor Wilma a job.

The public outcry was fierce,
They took Wilma from the farmer
And found her a job in a hotel
Which was being investigated by Panorama.

The hotel was run by a press baron
And lots of animals worked there.
The porter was an old goat,
The receptionist a stupid mare.

Now you may not believe this story
But I can tell you all now
That I have stayed in this hotel
Where the waiter was a pig and the cleaner a cow!

# Never Ask a Favour

Never ask a favour of a crab
Whatever you do.
He'll never listen,
He'll never help you.

Never ask a favour of a prawn
For he will just swim away,
He doesn't do favours
Or listen to what you say.

Never ask a favour of a clam,
Never ask him for any help,
He'll just clam up
And lay deep in the kelp.

The reason they won't help,
Or grant you what you wish,
Is because of what they are -
They're all shellfish!


# Teachers

Some teachers are so wonderful,
Some teachers are so cool,
Some teachers are so brilliant
But none of these teach at my school.

# Never Trust a Gerbil

I once had two gerbils,
I didn't want any more,
But after two weeks
They'd turned into four.

How could this happen?
I know they have to mix
But it was getting stupid
When they multiplied to six.

I tried to give them away
To my best friend Ben,
But when he called to see them
They'd multiplied to ten.

Now I had to stop them
From breeding any more
So I took them to the vet
And out popped another four!

The vet could do nothing,
It's the way that gerbils breed.
I now had twenty gerbils -
How many babies do they need?

Mum said to get rid of them
So I gave her my word,
I would get rid of every one
Or I'd end up with a gerbil herd.

So I tried to give them away
Just as fast as I could -
The little terrors kept on breeding,
I knew that they would.

But I would not be beaten
By a bunch of rapid rodents,
Though I don't know why the man
Took them for his science students!

## Boy Called Billy

There was once a boy called Billy
Who one day did something quite silly.
He tried to kill a big bee
While he was having a wee
And got stung on the end of his willy!

## Mr James Wears a Bra!

Mr James teaches drama,
He's so laid back, not hurried,
He told us that he's a thespian
Which really made me worried.

You see I saw him in a panto,
He really was the star.
He played an ugly sister
And I'm sure he wore a bra!

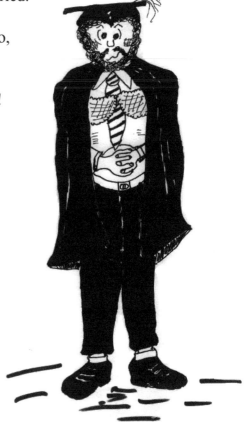

## The Romans

Romans conquered half the world
And many people they hurt.
I don't know how they managed it
When they were wearing skirts.

# I've Changed My Pants

I've started wearing trousers
Because I was feeling sick.
I'm growing far too tall
But I'm as skinny as a stick.

My mum explained the reason
But I don't know what she means,
She says that I'm just like dad,
She says it's in my jeans.

# Do Birds Wee?

I once saw a bird
High in a tree
And thought to myself
Do birds wee?

I know they pooh,
It covers dad's car!
But I've never seen one wee,
It's very peculiar.

They drink water,
I know that's true.
Maybe they wee
When they pooh.

# Dirty Barry

It was many years ago
In a field not far from here,
There lived a tough mouse
Who filled the rest with fear.

This mouse was not a local,
He came from over the sea,
A cat had scarred his face
Back in the land of Italy.

Now Scarface ran the field
Doing what he pleased,
He'd got all the other mice
Addicted to hard cheese.

The mayor mouse needed action,
He needed it in a hurry.
There was only one mouse for the job
And that was Dirty Barry.

Barry was a rough rodent
Expelled from the mouse force
For using too much violence,
Never showing any remorse.

Barry had worked the east field
And been expelled once or twice,
But he'd done so well in his new job
Working for the Miami mice.

But Barry wanted his old job back,
The mayor knew that he would.
Barry asked for his old side-kick,
Clint from the east wood.

So Barry and Clint, detectives,
Through the field started to crawl.
Soon they found that Scarface
Was really called Al Ca'awl.

The detectives knew what to do,
They had to cause a big freeze
And stop Al from smuggling in
His pasta and hard cheese.

This made Al so angry
That he said, "Hunt them down!
There's no place here for good guys,
This is Al Ca'awls town."

Soon there was a showdown,
They met up at the dock leaf.
The air was so tense,
No one dared to breathe.

Al talked to Barry and Clint,
"Get out of town!" he said,
But Barry quickly swung around
And fired a mouse pellet to Al's head.

Al's gang then started to panic,
Some just turned and fled.
When the pellet battle was over
Barry knew Al wasn't dead.

Al reached for his pistol
And Barry was heard to say,
"Did I fire five or six pellets?"
"Well punk, go on, make my day!"

Al dropped his pistol
And was taken to the nick,
Social worker mice moved in
Helping cheese addicts get better quick.

Barry and Clint were honoured
And Al was heard to sob,
"Why come back and ruin me?"
Barry replied, "I'm just doing my job!"

## The Princess and the Pee

I once read a story
About a princess and a pea,
It all sounds very silly
If you were to ask me.

To find the real princess
They placed a mattress on a pea
But the princess couldn't sleep,
Just why couldn't they see?

No one would sleep on it,
They must be wrong in the head,
Expecting her to sleep there
When they'd peed the bed!


## Confucius

There was an old Chinese man,
Confucius was his name,
Dishing out pearls of wisdom
Really was his game.

"Listen to this!" is a phrase
That he would often say.
"Man with hole in back pocket
Feel cheeky all day."

# Dad's Secret

Dad has a terrible secret
Which fills me full of dread -
I was looking in his bedroom
And found magazines under his bed.

I know that it's his business
What he reads when all alone,
But what if my friends knew
We had those magazines at home.

They would all laugh at me
And they'd call me a prat.
No one wants to hang around
With a kid whose dad does that.

One picture was terrible,
It was a real heart-stopper -
It's a picture of a big steam train!
Yes, my dad's a secret train-spotter!


# Betty Binns

Betty Binns, beautiful belle, bought
A big brown bread board.
"Buying big brown bread boards
Beggars belief!" boasted Betty Binns'
Big bad boyfriend Barry Black.

# The Mutant Hamster

We have a mutant hamster
That we bought from a laboratory,
He has big eyes and legs
And he's green and furry.

He sits out on a log,
Hiding in the weeds,
He hates eating flies
But loves eating seeds.

People think him strange,
Such an unusual pet.
He hates the water,
Doesn't like to get his fur wet.

People will often ask us
What we call this little monster.
We always smile as we reply,
"He goes by the name of Frogster."


# Young Man from Wapping

There was a young man from Wapping,
Who ran the world without stopping.
He said, "That was so neat!
But just look at my feet,
My blisters will not stop popping!"

## Food

Billy was a butcher,
His shop was on our street
But he had to close down
Because of infected meat.

George was a greengrocer,
To which he was well-suited,
But he had to close down
Because his produce was polluted.

Barney had a café,
It did not bring him wealth,
He too closed down -
It seems food is bad for our health.

## Keep Your Hair On!

I wanted to have my hair shaved,
I thought that it looked cool.
Now I wish I hadn't
I look such a stupid fool.

I didn't know I had big ears
Or that my head was small.
Dad said, "You remind me of
A flying billiard ball!"

## Young Boy from Surrey

There was a young boy from Surrey
Who would eat far too much curry.
He let off a huge fart
Which blew his trousers apart
And covered his room in slurry.

## The Lump

We had a new carpet fitted
And noticed a lump in the middle.
No one knew just what it was,
It really was a riddle.

Dad jumped up and down on it
Then hit it with a bat.
Mum tried to sit on it
But still it wouldn't go flat.

Though it had got smaller
Dad was getting in a rage
When my sister started crying
On seeing the hamster's empty cage.

## Matilda the Turkey

Matilda was a turkey,
She wasn't very bright,
She looked forward to Christmas
Matilda wasn't quite right!

The farmer over-fed her
Each and every day,
Matilda ate it all
But soon would have to pay.

The chickens tried to tell her
Of the danger she was in.
She thought them jealous,
They were scrawny and thin.

As Christmas drew near
The farm animals told her, 'Run!'
But Matilda was so fat
She couldn't get up off her bum.

Matilda tried to kid herself
Saying she didn't want to be thinner -
"The farmer likes me as I am,
He's even invited me over for dinner!"

She said, "I'm so excited,
I don't know what to wear."
A chicken said, "How about gravy?"
Which gave poor Matilda a scare.

The truth was finally spoken
By old Henry the horse:
"You're not going as a dinner guest
You're going as the main course!"

"Oh, my! What shall I do?"
Matilda was heard to shriek.
"I'll help," said Percy the pig,
"I'll disguise you as a sheep."

So the animals found some wool,
The chickens then made a suit
With two thin sticks for back legs -
Matilda looked quite cute.

So came Christmas Eve
And the farmer, in his vest,
Opened up the coup
To find a sheep sat on a nest.

The farmer said, "Well, I never!
Just how did you get in here?"
Matilda was so worried
She'd just laid an egg in fear.

As the farmer picked up Matilda
She nearly lost one false leg.
The farmer then screamed to his wife,
"Come quick! This sheep's laid an egg!"

The farmer's wife said, "It's Christmas,
You know what this means love?
I think we have a miracle!
It's a sign from up above."

So Matilda became famous
As the sheep that lays eggs,
Wobbling around the farmyard
On a pair of dodgy legs.

But she never forgot
The animals who saved her life,
So she shares out all the food
Given by the farmer's wife.

# Danny

Danny nicked the vicar's bike
Which caused such a commotion.
When the police caught up with him
They took him to the station.

They said that he was crazy,
They said that he was bad,
They said he was a loser,
They said that he was mad.

I know that they are wrong,
Danny's none of these
And until someone cares for him
Danny won't try to please.

The vicar dropped the charges,
Danny said, "Thanks very much."
He shook the vicar by the hand
And walked off with his watch!

## Mary's Pet

Mary had a turnip,
She kept it as a pet.
She thought it was ill
So she took it to the vet.

The vet shook his head
And told her what to do:
"Put it with other vegetables
And make yourself a stew."

## Mums New Boyfriend

Mum has a new partner
Who wants to be my friend.
He tries to act young and trendy,
He's driving me round the bend.

He shouts to me, "Yo, Wilf!"
Then tries to give me five.
I've never seen anything so stupid
As long as I've been alive.

I know he's not a bad man
And he's so good to mum,
But when will he realise
He was never, ever young!

# The Dreaded Mobile Phone

Mobile phones keep on ringing,
They're driving me insane
With their silly little ring tones,
They're eating at my brain.

People walk the streets,
Eyes rolling in their sockets.
If one mobile phone should ring
A hundred people scramble in their pockets.

From this scourge there's no escape,
There's always some one at your rear
Talking a load of inane tripe
With a phone pressed to their ear.

From the cinema to the bank,
Everywhere you should roam
Some prat's frying his brain
With the help of a mobile phone.

I know this makes me unpopular
But I don't think I'm alone,
There must be other people
Who feel the same about mobile phones.

So why don't we band together?
Let's all have some fun -
The next time some prat's phone rings
Give him a swift kick up the bum!

## Wally's Eating Worms

Just up the road,
At number twenty-three,
I had to go and baby-sit so
Jane, my girlfriend, came with me.

I had a cunning plan
As there was no one at home:
I'd put the kids to bed
And we would be alone.

I looked after two children,
Wally, who's three, Sally who's five,
They looked so sweet and innocent
But they could eat you alive.

So I put them to bed
And left on the light,
Went back down to Jane
Then got a terrible fright.

From upstairs a voice screamed,
"Wilf! Please come quick!
Wally's eaten toothpaste
And now he's being sick."

So I quickly ran upstairs -
Oh, what a mess!
Wally had thrown-up
Down Sally's nightdress.

So I cleaned them both up
And went back down to Jane,
We were trying for our first kiss
But those kids were a pain.

I took hold of Jane,
Held her in my arms,
Our lips drew closer,
She was falling for my charms.

Then a voice from upstairs screamed,
"Wilf! Urgh! They're full of germs.
Please! I need you! Come quick!
Stupid Wally's eating worms!

So I ran upstairs,
I was quite irate.
Where did he get them?
They were his dad's fishing bait.

There, hanging from his mouth,
A worm so long and thin.
I told him to spit it out
But he just sucked it in.

So back downstairs
Jane wasn't pleased,
She said, "Can't you see
That you're being teased!"

Then from upstairs a voice screamed,
"Wilf! Come quick! We need you!
Wally's been messing about
And his foot is stuck down the loo."

So I pulled out the brat
And I put them both to bed,
Went back to Jane
Who was going out of her head.

She said she was fed up
And that she wanted to go,
I told her they'd behave
Then I screamed out "Oh, no!"

Because a voice from upstairs said,
"Wilf! Please! I need some water."
Sally was standing there grinning,
Just like the devil's daughter.

I put them back to bed
Then I gave them a fright
By placing a very big teddy
In front of the landing light.

The teddy cast a shadow
Against their bedroom wall.
I said if they didn't go to sleep
This monster would pay them a call.

So I made up with Jane
By telling her this:
"Forget about the kids!
Just give me a kiss!"

# My Grandma is a Zulu

My Grandma is a Zulu!
She says it has its charms,
Dressed in long beautiful robes
And bangles up her arms.

All her hair is braided
With different coloured beads.
She doesn't live in Africa
But on a council estate in Leeds.

Yes, my Grandma is a Zulu!
People say she's such a sight
Just because she's a Zulu -
And both British and white!


# Spelling Made Easy

Why R these words not spelled like this?
Why 'Y'
Bee 'B'
Sea 'C'
Eye 'I'
You 'U'
Pea 'P'
Are 'R'
Tea 'T'
Ask your teachers Y.

## Tommy the Hamster R.I.P.

Tommy was my little hamster
Who one day died of flu,
So I wrapped him in some toilet roll
And flushed him down the loo.

## Killer Goldfish

My dad bought a goldfish
From a man down the pub.
He said, "It's from Brazil,
And it don't half like its grub!"

But when I tried to feed it
It started behaving quite odd,
Biting at my fingers,
The vicious little sod.

It didn't look much like a goldfish
It was so big beyond belief,
With evil staring eyeballs
And nasty looking teeth.

I showed my friend my goldfish.
"I know it's not a charmer!"
He said, "It's not a goldfish -
What you have is a Brazilian Piranha!"

## Heavens a Bug!

Poor Barney the bug died
And went off to bug heaven,
Deeply missed by all his kids,
All one million and twenty seven.

He reached bugs' pearly gates,
There was a bug with golden feet
Who asked Barney his name
Then said, "They call me Pete."

Barney filled in a form,
He thought it was a dream.
They asked him how he'd died:
"On a car windscreen."

So he entered bugs' heaven
To meet the maker of all bugs,
Everyone was so lovely -
He received five billion hugs.

# The Name's Grandad

Grandad says he's a secret agent
Who always works alone.
No one would suspect his H.Q.
Is the Sunny Bank Old Folks Home.

His wheelchair's his Aston Martin,
It's electric with many speeds,
It's got many hidden gadgets,
Loads more than he needs.

He's an expert with weapons
And a master of kung fu,
But since he lost his teeth
He finds it difficult to chew.

He says he speaks many languages
And that he's proud to be British,
But Grandad's just an old man
Who speaks a lot of rubbish.

I used to love his stories
When I was very young,
But now I'm older and cool
They don't seem so much fun.

# Barbara's Big Bum

I know a woman called Barbara,
She's a friend of my mum,
Who's obsessed with her image,
Thinking she has a big bum.

Wearing far too much make-up
She says with a hiss,
"Please tell me your opinion -
Does my bum look big in this?"

My mum has often told her,
When she comes to call,
"It's not your bum that's big,
It's your skirt that's too small!"

But Barbara will not listen,
She thinks she's so young.
Telling dad she was thirty-two
He asked, "How old is your bum?"

Then Barbara lost her temper,
Flew into a violent rage
As dad said, "Add ten more years
And you'll be nearer your real age."

So why does she do it?
No one really knows.
She would look so nice
If she wore the right size clothes.

## Disgusting Doris

Doris is such a bad girl
Who always tries to trick us,
She wears her skirts far too short -
You can often see her knickers!

Chewing gum in class,
Blowing bubbles that pop
With gum all around her face
But still Doris will not stop.

Doris picks her nose and eats it -
What a disgusting little creature;
You'd think the school would step in
And find us a better teacher.

## Batman is a Softy

Batman is a softy,
He runs away from fights,
Scared of breaking a fingernail
Then laddering his new tights.

## Isaac Newton

There was once a man called Isaac Newton
Who, it is said,
Discovered the law of gravity
When an apple fell on his head.

So this is the law
He discovered that day:
What goes up must come down.
"Wow!" I hear you say.

Well, it's not true.
My kite got stuck up a tree
It's been there ten years
Since I was three!

## Smelly Girlfriend

My girlfriend loves garlic,
She eats it day and night.
She says it keeps her healthy
But I don't think that's right.

Although she's good looking
Her breath just makes me reel,
And when I have to snog her
I know just how vampires feel!

# GigAUNTtic

My auntie is so overweight
That she can't see her feet.
She says she's big boned -
I think it's the food she eats.

She eats so much food
Her dresses are like a tent,
And if she has big bones
She's the skeleton of an elephant.

## Our Teacher is a Tortoise

Our teacher is a tortoise,
His shell it forms a hunch,
By the time he's finished register
It's time to have our lunch.

He finds it hard to walk
And has little intellect,
But then he is a tortoise
So what would you expect?

Other classes are no better
Taught by monkeys and a gnu,
The head teacher's an elephant,
It's like learning in a zoo!

We are all so fed up
And don't know what to do.
Animals don't use toilets
So the corridors are filled with pooh.

I know this sounds strange,
It's such a terrible state,
We treated our teachers badly
So they became very irate.

Soon they started leaving
In ones, then in twos,
So animals were brought in
Because they were closing the zoos.

We finally begged our teachers
To come back to our school
Otherwise we would have grown up
Just a bunch of stupid fools.

So the animals were removed
And the teachers returned, of course,
Except for Mr Rix of class six,
I'm sure that he's a horse!

# The Indestructible Bogey

Have you ever had a bogey
That's so far up your nose
So you could never pick it,
Well, I had one of those.

I tried with each finger
But it wouldn't come out,
I even tried sucking it
Using the vacuum's spout.

I've used pens, pencils
And a long cotton bud,
I tried it with a paper-clip,
Even a piece of wood.

Then mum shouted at me
For making such a show.
"For heaven's sake stop messing,
And give your nose a blow!"

# Not a Prayer

Our vicar is so holy,
Our vicar is without sin.
I've seen him in the betting shop
Praying for a horse to win.

## My Mum's a Werewolf

My mum is a werewolf,
She howls a lot at night
And she is very hairy,
Not such a pretty sight.

Dad, he didn't know
That when he got wed
He was marrying a werewolf,
Mum should have said.

It's embarrassing to have a werewolf
As part of your kin.
Dad thought she was a vampire,
Just like me and him.

# The Fisherman and the Fish

Once there was a fish,
Swimming in the sea,
That bit on a hook
To get a meal for free.

He twisted and turned,
Putting up such a fight
But he knew he was losing
As he drifted to the light.

Would this be the end
Of our very brave fish?
Is his future to lay
In someone's dish?

The fisherman was pleased,
It was a meal for free
When the fish looked up
Saying, "Please, kill me!"

The fisherman was shocked,
This fish was speaking!
In his little boat
That was slowly leaking.

"In all my life I've never seen
A fish that wanted to die."
The fish it gasped for breath
As it stared up at the sky.

The fisherman picked it up
And put it back in the sea.
The fish he begged and pleaded,
"Please, please kill me!"

The fisherman let the fish go
Saying, "Why do you want to die?"
The fish swam away laughing
Saying, "I don't! I told a lie!"

So let this be a lesson,
If killing is your wish,
You must be quite stupid
To be outsmarted by a fish!

# Dad Wears Mum's Tights!

My dad is a joiner,
He works on building sites.
When it's freezing cold
He wears my mother's tights.

He says it keeps his legs warm,
My mum she makes a fuss
As his hairs poke through the tights
And make his legs look like a cactus!

## Jack and Jill

Jack and Jill went up the hill
For just what, do you think?
All that way for a drop of water
When they could've used the sink.

Jack fell down and broke his crown,
Now that's a very strange thing.
Why would he be wearing a crown
When he isn't even a king?

And what about stupid Jill,
She was filled with such laughter.
She didn't look, tripped up
Then went a-tumbling after.

Then up Jack got, stupid clot,
Just what was his caper?
You'd think he'd go to the hospital
Not wrap his head in vinegar and paper!


## Comput*rrs

CoMputers are GOO£d,
Computerrrs are bAd,
W*hen* _they_ **don't** wo
rk
th"y drive me m^d.

## The One and Only

Paul is small,
Saul is tall,
Nick is thick,
Mick is quick,
Lynne is thin,
Pat is fat,
Pete is neat,
Gerty is dirty.
I am different
From all the rest,
Pleased to meet you,
I'm the best!

## Confucius II (This Time it's Personal)

Confucius was a wise man,
This was asked of him:
Do you have to be crackers
To live in a biscuit tin?

## Terry's Tidgy Tonsils

Terry had a sore throat
So the doctor checked him out.
Terry couldn't even talk
And he loved to scream and shout.

"I've found the cause of your problem,
It was so easy to spot.
"You've got such tidgy tonsils
Because they've started to rot."

So Terry had an operation,
His tidgy tonsils were pulled out,
But his mum isn't too happy
Now Terry can scream and shout.

# Smashing Trick

There was once a great magician
Who performed a magic trick
Using what's known as sleight of hand,
He had to be very, very quick.

He asked a man for his watch
Then placed it in a sack
And smashed it with a hammer -
The man asked for it back.

The magician said not to worry
And in the bat of an eye
Produced, as if from nowhere,
A very large pork pie.

Well, what do you think was in it?
The man broke it open with a sigh -
It was filled with pork you idiot,
That's why it's called a pork pie!

# Bertie the Pig

Bertie was a pig
Who said his back was aching.
The farmer said, "It could be worse,
You could be crispy bacon!"

## Take a Seat

Jenny had to go to hospital
Which wasn't such a treat -
Someone had squirted superglue
All over the toilet seat.

Jenny had sat down
To do what must be done,
But when she stood back up
The seat was stuck to her bum!

A blanket covered poor Jenny,
The whole school let out a cheer
As she waddled through the playground
With the seat stuck to her rear.

A man then took her details,
He said, "My name's Pete."
He told her not to worry,
"Now please, just take a seat."

A nurse took out some pliers,
Jenny let out a scream.
The nurse said, "Don't worry,
They're to open a jar of cream!

So the seat was removed,
Jenny now knows what to do:
Always check the toilet seat
Before you sit down on the loo!

## Tonight We Saw a Young Boy

Tonight we saw a young boy,
He was sleeping on the street.
People just ignored him,
He was getting under their feet.

Tonight we saw a young boy,
He was cold and in pain.
No one knows where he's from,
No one knows his name.

Tonight we saw a young boy,
He made me want to cry
But we didn't stop to offer help,
Just looked away and passed him by.